Big Dinosaur Sticker Book

Illustrated by Paul Nicholls
Designed by Vicky Arrowsmith
Written by Fiona Watt

Contents

You will find all the stickers at the back of the book.

The first dinosaurs

About 225 million years ago, a long, long time before people ever existed, the first dinosaurs roamed the land.

Fill the pages with stickers of small dinosaurs scurrying around, along with the other strange scaly reptiles that lived at that time.

Massive monsters

Brachiosaurus, Diplodocus and Apatosaurus, with their long necks and strong tails, were longer than two buses parked end to end. They were among the biggest dinosaurs that ever lived, even though they only ate plants.

Use the stickers to fill the scene with hungry dinosaurs.

Duck-billed dinosaurs

Hadrosaurs were plant-eaters with hard, beak-like mouths. They also made honking noises by blowing air through the hollow horns on their heads.

Use the stickers to fill the pages with herds of hadrosaurs.

Under the sea

At the same time that dinosaurs lived on land, other creatures called plesiosaurs lived in the sea. They had long necks and four flippers, that they flapped up and down as they swam.

Fill the sea with plesiosaurs and other prehistoric sea creatures.

Baby dinosaurs

Baby dinosaurs hatched out of eggs. This mother Maiasaura made a mound of sand and laid her eggs on it. Then, she covered them with leaves to keep them safe and warm.

Press on the egg stickers and hatching babies.

T-rex

Bigger than an elephant, with powerful jaws and dagger-like teeth, Tyrannosaurus rex was a massive meat-eating dinosaur that prowled through forests.

Press on the stickers of the terrified dinosaurs trying to escape.

Attack

Small dinosaurs often hunted in packs. They would attack a much bigger dinosaur, slashing it with their claws and biting its back.

Press on the stickers of vicious Deinonychus dinosaurs attacking a Tenontosaurus.

Bony backs

No one really knows why Stegosaurs had a row of bony plates running down their backs. They may have been to soak up heat from the Sun or for protection. They also had nasty spikes, for swiping at enemies, on their tails.

Fill the pages with a herd of Stegosaurs.

Up in the air

Dinosaurs couldn't fly, but reptiles called pterosaurs lived at the same time as the dinosaurs. They had furry bodies and huge, leathery wings.

Add the stickers of pterosaurs swooping over the sea, trying to catch fish to eat.

Hungry herbivores

Many enormous dinosaurs didn't eat meat, but only ate plants and leaves. Their incredibly long necks allowed them to reach the tops of trees.

Fill the pages with Brachiosaurus dinosaurs nibbling leaves with their sharp, chisel-like teeth.

19

Three horns

Triceratops had two long, sharp horns on their heads and a shorter one on their noses. They may have lived in herds, that would surround their young to protect them from danger.

Fill the pages with Triceratops stickers protecting their babies from a hungry T-rex.

The end of the dinosaurs

Dinosaurs died out about 65 million years ago, but no one is certain why. Some scientists think that a massive rock fell from space, creating fires, earthquakes and huge clouds of dust. The dust blocked out light from the Sun and killed all the plants that lots of dinosaurs ate.

Fill the pages with frightened dinosaurs trying to escape.

What came next?

After the dinosaurs died out, furry mammals took their place. These creatures were warm-blooded and gave birth to babies rather than laying eggs.

Fill the page with squirrel-like creatures scampering around the forest.

The first dinosaurs

Saltopus

Coelophysis

Desmatosuchus

Stagonolepis

Compsognathus

Shuvosaurus

Dromomeron

Vancleavea

Terrestrisuchus

Massive monsters

Camarasaurus

Allosaurus

Apatosaurus

Brachiosaurus

Diplodocus

Duck-billed dinosaurs

Quetzalcoatlus

Corythosaurus

Lambeosaurus

Parasaurolophus

Corythosaurus

Under the sea

Pterosaurs

Peloneustes

Fish

Pycnodont

Ichthyosaur

Ammonite

Belemnites

Sea scorpion

Pages 8-9

Baby dinosaurs

Maiasaura hatchlings

Pages 10-11

T-rex

Troodon

Dromaeosaur

Compsognathus

Ornitholestes

Sinornithosaurus

Attack

Page 12

Deinonychus

Page 13

Bony backs

Stegosaurus

Ornitholestes

Ceratosaurus

Up in the air

Pteranodon

Rhamphorhynchus

Pterodactyl

Hungry herbivores

Brachiosaurus

Pterosaur

Three horns

Triceratops

Ornitholestes

End of the dinosaurs

Parasaurolophus

Pterosaur

T-rex

Triceratops

Stegosaurus

Ankylosaurus

Velociraptor

Carnotaurus

Pages 22-23

What came next?

Zalambdalestes

Purgatorius

Ptilodus

Plesiadapis

Ischyromys

Chriacus

Megazostrodon